Jacqueline Wilson

ILLUSTRATED BY NICK SHARRATT

DIARY 2017

DOUBLEDAY

HAVE YOU READ THEM ALL?

FAMILY DRAMAS
THE BED AND BREAKFAST STAR
CANDYFLOSS
CLEAN BREAK
COOKIE
FOUR CHILDREN AND IT
THE ILLUSTRATED MUM
KATY
LILY ALONE
LITTLE DARLINGS
LOLA ROSE
THE LONGEST WHALE SONG
MIDNIGHT
THE SUITCASE KID

MOST POPULAR CHARACTERS
HETTY FEATHER
SAPPHIRE BATTERSEA
EMERALD STAR
DIAMOND
LITTLE STARS
THE STORY OF TRACY BEAKER
THE DARE GAME
STARRING TRACY BEAKER

STORIES ABOUT SISTERS
THE BUTTERFLY CLUB
THE DIAMOND GIRLS
DOUBLE ACT
THE WORST THING
ABOUT MY SISTER

FOR OLDER READERS

DUSTBIN BABY
GIRLS IN LOVE
GIRLS IN TEARS
GIRLS OUT LATE
GIRLS UNDER PRESSURE
KISS
LOVE LESSONS
MY SISTER JODIE

ALSO AVAILABLE
PAWS AND WHISKERS
THE JACQUELINE WILSON
CHRISTMAS CRACKER
THE JACQUELINE WILSON
TREASURY

VISIT JACQUELINE'S FANTASTIC WEBSITE!

There's a whole Jacqueline Wilson town to explore! You can generate your own special username, customize your online bedroom, test your knowledge of Jacqueline's books with fun quizzes and puzzles, and upload book reviews. There's lots of fun stuff to discover, including competitions, book trailers, and Jacqueline's scrapbook. And if you love writing, visit the special storytelling area! Plus, you can hear the latest news from Jacqueline in her monthly diary, find out whether she's doing events near you, read her fan-mail replies, and chat to other fans on the message boards!

www.jacquelinewilson.co.uk

THIS DIARY BELONGS TO:

HERE'S A
PHOTO OF ME!

If found, please contact: _____

Address: _____

_____

_____

_____

Phone number: _____

GEMS AND JEWELS

I've always been fascinated by gems and jewels.
When I was little, I loved to play with my grandma's
button box. I sifted through her collection of red
and green and blue buttons, and pretended they
were precious rubies and emeralds and sapphires.
I loved to try on my grandma's modest diamond
ring and my mum's small emerald engagement ring.

I longed to wear jewellery too, but only had a
glass ring out of a Christmas cracker
and a few thin plastic bangles. Look
at me now! When I had my first
book published, I treated myself
to a lovely big amethyst ring, and
I've kept on buying them ever since.
At one time I wore a ring on every
finger, even my two thumbs, and
although I'm more restrained now, I
still have lots of silver bangles that
jingle away whenever I move my
arms. My daughter, Emma, says it's
very useful when she temporarily

loses me in a big shop or gallery – all she has to do is listen for the jingling.

I'm still fascinated by all the different kinds of gemstones, and enjoy giving many of my fictional heroines jewel names. I wonder how many you can think of?

I treasure all my own jewellery, especially a rose-quartz ring given as a present, because it's supposed to represent unconditional love.

Perhaps the true gems in life are the people you love and who love you.

Jacqueline Wilson

HOW TO DRAW
DIAMOND'S TIARA

Diamond wears a pretty tiara when she's performing.
Have a go at designing one yourself following these
easy instructions by Nick Sharratt.

1. Start with an arc of pearls.

2. Position a few large gemstones.

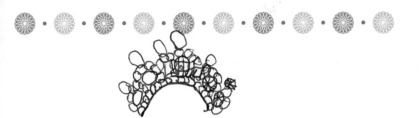

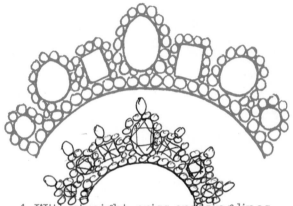

3. Frame the stones with more pearls.

4. With straight, criss-crossing lines,
turn the stones into cut jewels.

NICK'S COLOURING TIPS!

Shade one or two facets lighter than the
rest, and your jewels will sparkle.

Highlights add real shine.

Colour the jewels in rich hues like
ruby red, sapphire blue or emerald green.

RUBY AND GARNET'S PUZZLE PAGES!

Challenge yourself with this sparkling array
of puzzles courtesy of everyone's favourite
identical twins! You'll find the answers at
the back of the book.

WHO IS THIS?

Like Ruby and Garnet in *Double Act*, many of the
characters in Jacqueline's stories are named after
precious stones. Who is describing herself in
each of the extracts below? *opal*

1. I was top of the class. I couldn't seem to help it.
It meant that some teachers liked me and made me
their pet, while other teachers like Mounty seemed
to resent me bitterly. I tried hard to make the
other girls like me, but most of them despised me.
They considered it shameful to be such a
swot – though what else did they expect from
a scholarship girl? *Ruby*

2. I choose for both of us. T-shirts. Leggings. Jeans. Matching ones, of course.

rby

3. I used to be called Ellen-Jane Potts, but my dear friend Hetty says it doesn't matter a jot if you change your name. She has changed her name three times. She calls herself Emerald Star for all the shows – and now she has fashioned herself an emerald-green riding jacket and has shiny swashbuckling boots to stride about in.

Dimond

WORD SEARCH

There are ten sparkly stones hidden in this word search – can you find them all?

N	Q	D	K	W	T	V	B	L	R	X	M	F	O	I
Y	L	N	F	G	T	U	X	F	F	L	D	I	P	T
N	G	I	Z	E	F	A	R	P	J	R	C	G	A	D
J	C	C	N	L	G	J	X	Q	P	E	A	R	L	M
A	S	R	Z	X	S	X	Q	W	U	S	M	K	J	X
V	A	V	Y	Y	A	X	B	X	D	O	G	Q	P	F
G	V	T	T	C	P	M	C	Z	R	O	I	A	W	O
X	Y	M	O	H	P	N	H	D	F	U	M	S	U	D
H	U	H	D	G	H	H	X	Y	L	E	B	J	E	S
S	S	X	I	Y	I	M	Y	S	T	A	L	Y	R	T
M	U	Y	R	I	R	S	I	H	U	P	R	T	Z	C
D	Z	C	E	G	E	D	Y	R	Y	F	D	E	P	A
Z	G	C	P	W	J	S	L	Q	X	F	K	C	M	A
C	C	T	H	T	T	D	N	O	M	A	I	D	F	E
L	M	V	H	Q	V	G	S	F	L	H	E	J	W	W

AMETHYST   DIAMOND   EMERALD
GARNET   OPAL   PEARL   PERIDOT
RUBY   SAPPHIRE   TURQUOISE

BIRTHSTONES
AND BIRTHDAYS

The custom of wearing precious stones associated with the month you were born is thought to have started over 2000 years ago! Sparkly stones are very nice to look at, but the real gems in life are the people closest to us. Fill in your friends' birthdays in the following table.

JANUARY **BIRTHSTONE: GARNET** The origin of the word garnet comes from the Latin word *granatus*, which means seed.	*Grandad L*
FEBRUARY **BIRTHSTONE: AMETHYST** Ancient Egyptians loved the soft purple colour of amethysts and often used them in jewellery.	
MARCH **BIRTHSTONE: AQUAMARINE** The biggest aquamarine gemstone was found in Marambaia, Minas Gerais, Brazil in 1910. It weighed over 110kg!	
APRIL **BIRTHSTONE: DIAMOND** Diamond is only one of many forms of the element carbon found naturally on Earth. Another form is graphite – which is used to make pencil lead!	*Maurus Mum*

MAY BIRTHSTONE: EMERALD One of the world's most famous uncut emeralds is called the Duke of Devonshire Emerald. It weighs about 276g!	
JUNE BIRTHSTONE: PEARL Pearls are made when a grain of sand or grit enters the soft body of an oyster or mussel. Layers form around the grain to make the beautiful shiny pearl.	Nana
JULY BIRTHSTONE: RUBY In ancient times, rubies were laid underneath the foundations of new buildings for good luck.	Edith
AUGUST BIRTHSTONE: PERIDOT Peridot is an olive-green stone which is often found in volcanic lava.	

SEPTEMBER BIRTHSTONE: SAPPHIRE Not all sapphires are blue – there are also pink, yellow and green sapphires. Very rare *padparadscha* sapphires are orange.	Emily B ✓
OCTOBER BIRTHSTONE: OPAL Opal is the national gemstone of Australia. Opals are multi-coloured stones which come in many different combinations of colours.	Grandad
NOVEMBER BIRTHSTONE: CITRINE The lemon-coloured citrine stone gets its name from the Latin word citrina, which means yellow.	Vidal b
DECEMBER BIRTHSTONE: TURQUOISE Turquoise stones were used to create the lighter blue bands on Ancient Egyptian King Tutankhamun's famous burial mask.	Lisa B

MY TIMETABLE

	MONDAY	TUESDAY
9.00am		
9.30am		
10.00am		
10.30am		
11.00am		
11.30am		
12.00pm		
12.30pm		
13.00pm		
13.30pm		
14.00pm		
14.30pm		
15.00pm		
15.30pm		
16.00pm	End of day	
16.30pm		

MY TIMETABLE

WEDNESDAY	THURSDAY	FRIDAY

Monday 26

Tuesday 27

Wednesday 28

Thursday 29

Friday 30

Saturday 31

Sunday 1

Notes

Monday 2

Tuesday 3

Wednesday 4

Thursday 5

Friday 6

Saturday 7

Sunday 8 got doiry and toching ponys whith family and looking for the rabits down by the pound

Notes

Monday 9

Tuesday 10

Wednesday 11

Thursday 12

Friday 13

Saturday 14

Sunday 15

'You're my special grown-up daughter, Emerald,' said Dad.
    My name isn't *really* Emerald, it's plain Emily. All the rest of
the family called me Em. I loved it when Dad called me Emerald.

From CLEAN BREAK

Monday 16

Tuesday 17

Wednesday 18

Thursday 19

Friday 20

Saturday 21

Sunday 22

Notes

Monday 23

Tuesday 24

Wednesday 25

Thursday 26

Friday 27

Saturday 28

Sunday 29

Notes

Monday 30

Tuesday 31

Wednesday 1

Thursday 2

Friday 3

Saturday 4

Sunday 5

Notes

Monday 6

Tuesday 7

Wednesday 8

Thursday 9

Friday 10

Saturday 11

Sunday 12

'And what name did they christen you?'

I took a deep breath. 'Hetty Feather, but—'

'No buts! That is your name, and you will not be known by any other. Sapphire indeed!'

Yes, Sapphire, Sapphire, Sapphire, I said silently inside my head. *It is a beautiful name and it is my name, and you can 'Hetty Feather' me a thousand times a day, but I know my real name now and you cannot take it away from me.*

From SAPPHIRE BATTERSEA

Monday 13

Tuesday 14

Wednesday 15

Thursday 16

Friday 17

Saturday 18

Sunday 19

Notes

Monday 20

Tuesday 21

Wednesday 22

Thursday 23

Friday 24

Saturday 25

Sunday 26

Notes

Monday 27

Tuesday 28

Wednesday 1

Thursday 2

Friday 3

Saturday 4

Sunday 5

Notes

Monday 6

Tuesday 7

Wednesday 8

Thursday 9

Friday 10

Saturday 11

Sunday 12

'A crown!' I gasped, staring at the wonderful sparkling gems.
'A diamond crown!'

'No, dear, a tiara – and these stones are only glass. But it looks
pretty in the ring and the diamonds catch the light. Perfect for
little Diamond, the Acrobatic Child Wonder!'

From DIAMOND

Monday 13

Tuesday 14

Wednesday 15

Thursday 16

Friday 17

Saturday 18

Sunday 19

Notes

MARCH

Monday 20

Tuesday 21

Wednesday 22

Thursday 23

Friday 24

Saturday 25

Sunday 26

Notes

Monday 27

Tuesday 28

Wednesday 29

Thursday 30

Friday 31

Saturday 1

Sunday 2

Notes

Monday 3

Tuesday 4

Wednesday 5

Thursday 6

Friday 7

Saturday 8

Sunday 9

Notes

Monday 10

Tuesday 11

Wednesday 12

Thursday 13

Friday 14

Saturday 15

Sunday 16

I didn't have any jewellery at all, certainly not opals. I saw the prices of the opal necklaces in the jewellery shop and grew frightened. 'No, Morgan. No, absolutely not,' I said.

But he spotted a slim silver chain hanging on a black velvet stand at the back of the display. It had a small opal pendant in the shape of a teardrop. 'That looks perfect,' he said.

From OPAL PLUMSTEAD

Monday 17

Tuesday 18

Wednesday 19

Thursday 20

Friday 21

Saturday 22

Sunday 23

Notes

Monday 24

Tuesday 25

Wednesday 26

Thursday 27

Friday 28

Saturday 29

Sunday 30

Notes

Monday 1

Tuesday 2

Wednesday 3

Thursday 4

Friday 5

Saturday 6

Sunday 7

Notes

Monday 8

Tuesday 9

Wednesday 10

Thursday 11

Friday 12

Saturday 13

Sunday 14

Go on then. You got to the ring bit. Dad gave Mum the ring.

Richard gave Opal a beautiful opal ring, milky-white but with all different pinks and blues and greens and purples, sparkling like magic whenever it caught the light.

From DOUBLE ACT

Monday 15

Tuesday 16

Wednesday 17

Thursday 18

Friday 19

Saturday 20

Sunday 21

Notes

Monday 22

Tuesday 23

Wednesday 24

Thursday 25

Friday 26

Saturday 27

Sunday 28

Notes

Monday 29

Tuesday 30

Wednesday 31

Thursday 1

Friday 2

Saturday 3

Sunday 4

Notes

The talented gems of stage and screen, identical twins Ruby and Garnet Barker, who first sprang to stardom in the acclaimed television serial, 'The Twins at St Clare's.'

onday 5

night

Tidy bed whith toys ✓
Get beads op floor ✓
~~Op toys~~

Tuesday 6

Track
Morning Epretan   7:00
                         20 mins cri
· relax· wake dad· Make tea have
· have ~~Get begget~~ apetan ✓   break
   breakfeest · Get ~~dressed~~   20 mo
                                    me

Wednesday 7

mide   morning
· go outside · tak dad if a
can drive track
get taught · Put ipad of charge

Thursday 8

Afternoon

have snack· Do home work
whach TV whith fam

Friday 9

night

brig First Aid kit masusi

pack bag for tmrow

tsk mum if breng ipod

breu

Saturday 10

morning

have shower. do hair

chose outfit have

break

Sunday 11

mid morning

Take the stuff out

u put in bag then pleay

'Typical!' said Rochelle, pushing past to wave her grubby mop over the balcony. 'I do all the hard work, scrubbing away like stupid Cinderella, ruining my only decent jeans in the process, and she gets all this fussing. How come manky old Martine's your favourite, Mum?'

'You're all my favourite Diamond girls,' said Mum. 'Little sparkling gems, the lot of you – especially the pretty one with the Marigold gloves.'

From DIAMOND GIRLS

Monday 12

Tuesday 13

Wednesday 14

Thursday 15

Friday 16

Saturday 17

Sunday 18

Notes

Monday 19

Tuesday 20

Wednesday 21

Thursday 22

Friday 23

Saturday 24

Sunday 25

Notes

Monday 26

Tuesday 27

Wednesday 28

Thursday 29

Friday 30

Saturday 1

Sunday 2

Notes

Monday 3

Tuesday 4

Wednesday 5

Thursday 6

Friday 7

Saturday 8

Sunday 9

Notes

Monday 10

Tuesday 11

Wednesday 12

Thursday 13

Friday 14

Saturday 15

Sunday 16

I liked a stall of semi-precious stones. I stayed there for ages, fingering the smooth agate and amethyst and crystal pebbles while the stallholder told me they'd bring me love and luck and happiness. I wanted them all.

From CLEAN BREAK

Monday 17

Tuesday 18

Wednesday 19

Thursday 20

Friday 21

Saturday 22

Sunday 23

Notes

Monday 24

Tuesday 25

Wednesday 26

Thursday 27

Friday 28

Saturday 29

Sunday 30

Notes

Monday 31

Tuesday 1

Wednesday 2

Thursday 3

Friday 4

Saturday 5

Sunday 6

Notes

Monday 7

Tuesday 8

Wednesday 9

Thursday 10

Friday 11

Saturday 12

Sunday 13

'What?' said Bertie. 'Look, I like you being so small. It makes me feel almost big, see. And you've got a dear little face, with the biggest blue eyes.'

'Yes, they are my best feature. Sapphire blue.'

'There you are, then. And you don't need any bright fancy clothes, not with your flaming hair. It's all the colour you need.'

From SAPPHIRE BATTERSEA

Monday 14

Tuesday 15

Wednesday 16

Thursday 17

Friday 18

Saturday 19

Sunday 20

Notes

Monday 21

Tuesday 22

Wednesday 23

Thursday 24

Friday 25

Saturday 26

Sunday 27

Notes

Monday 28

Tuesday 29

Wednesday 30

Thursday 31

Friday 1

Saturday 2

Sunday 3

Notes

Monday 4

Tuesday 5

Wednesday 6

Thursday 7

Friday 8

Saturday 9

Sunday 10

Notes

Monday 11

Tuesday 12

Wednesday 13

Thursday 14

Friday 15

Saturday 16

Sunday 17

'Yes, we are children,' I said, my voice firmer now. 'That is the whole point. We are child artistes. This is Diamond, the Acrobatic Child Wonder. And I am Miss Emerald Star, Compère Extraordinaire. We have an appointment with Mrs Ruby, so we'd be grateful if you'd show us to her office.'

From LITTLE STARS

Monday 18

Tuesday 19

Wednesday 20

Thursday 21

Friday 22

Saturday 23

Sunday 24

Notes

Monday 25

Tuesday 26

Wednesday 27

Thursday 28

Friday 29

Saturday 30

Sunday 1

Notes

Monday 2

Tuesday 3

Wednesday 4

Thursday 5

Friday 6

Saturday 7

Sunday 8

Notes

Monday 9

Tuesday 10

Wednesday 11

Thursday 12

Friday 13

Saturday 14

Sunday 15

Neither of us looked like Marigold, though we both had a hint of her green eyes.

'Witch's eyes,' Marigold always said. Star's eyes were bluey-green, mine more grey green.

Marigold's eyes were emerald, the deepest glittery green, the green of summer meadows and seaweed and secret pools. Sometimes Marigold's eyes glittered so wildly it was as if they were spinning in her head like Catherine wheels, giving off sparks.

From THE ILLUSTRATED MUM

Monday 16

Tuesday 17

Wednesday 18

Thursday 19

Friday 20

Saturday 21

Sunday 22

Notes

Monday 23

Tuesday 24

Wednesday 25

Thursday 26

Friday 27

Saturday 28

Sunday 29

Notes

Monday 30

Tuesday 31

Wednesday 1

Thursday 2

Friday 3

Saturday 4

Sunday 5

Notes

Monday 6

Tuesday 7

Wednesday 8

Thursday 9

Friday 10

Saturday 11

Sunday 12

Perhaps it was going to be simple. I just had to take a quick turn about the village, see a red-haired man, and approach him. But then what? How was I to announce myself? *Hello, dear Father, I am your long-lost daughter. I am Hetty.* No, Sapphire. Emerald? Perhaps I wouldn't need to say a word. He would just catch a glimpse of me, stop short – and then open his arms. I would go running and he would hug me close, his red head bent to mine, holding me as if he could never bear to let me go.

From EMERALD STAR

Monday 13

Tuesday 14

Wednesday 15

Thursday 16

Friday 17

Saturday 18

Sunday 19

Notes

Monday 20

Tuesday 21

Wednesday 22

Thursday 23

Friday 24

Saturday 25

Sunday 26

Notes

Monday 27

Tuesday 28

Wednesday 29

Thursday 30

Friday 1

Saturday 2

Sunday 3

Notes

Monday 4

Tuesday 5

Wednesday 6

Thursday 7

Friday 8

Saturday 9

Sunday 10

Notes

Monday 11

Tuesday 12

Wednesday 13

Thursday 14

Friday 15

Saturday 16

Sunday 17

She'd spread an electric blue and silver Indian veil over the duvet
and turned her ordinary bed into a bower. It was sewn with red
jewels like rubies. When Jasmine lit the candles on her shelf
the jewels glowed in the flickering light. They were scented
candles, musky, sweet.

From MIDNIGHT

Monday 18

Tuesday 19

Wednesday 20

Thursday 21

Friday 22

Saturday 23

Sunday 24

Notes

Monday 25

Tuesday 26

Wednesday 27

Thursday 28

Friday 29

Saturday 30

Sunday 31

Notes

Monday 1

Tuesday 2

Wednesday 3

Thursday 4

PUZZLE ANSWERS!

WHO IS THIS?

1. Opal in OPAL PLUMSTEAD
2. Ruby in DOUBLE ACT
3. Diamond in DIAMOND

WORD SEARCH

N	Q	D	K	W	T	V	B	L	R	X	M	F	O	I
Y	L	N	F	G	T	U	X	F	F	L	D	I	P	T
N	G	I	Z	E	F	A	R	P	J	R	C	G	A	D
J	C	C	N	L	G	J	X	Q	P	E	A	R	L	M
A	S	R	Z	X	S	X	Q	W	U	S	M	K	J	X
V	A	V	Y	Y	A	X	B	X	D	O	G	Q	P	F
G	V	T	T	C	P	M	C	Z	R	O	I	A	W	O
X	Y	M	O	H	P	N	H	D	F	U	M	S	U	D
H	U	H	D	G	H	H	X	Y	L	E	B	J	E	S
S	S	X	I	Y	I	M	Y	S	T	A	L	Y	R	T
M	U	Y	R	I	R	S	I	H	U	P	R	T	Z	C
D	Z	C	E	G	E	D	Y	R	Y	F	D	E	P	A
Z	G	C	P	W	J	S	L	Q	X	F	K	C	M	A
C	C	T	H	T	T	D	N	O	M	A	I	D	F	E
L	M	V	H	Q	V	G	S	F	L	H	E	J	W	W

DOUBLEDAY

UK | USA | Canada | Ireland | Australia
India | New Zealand | South Africa

Doubleday is part of the Penguin Random House group of companies
whose addresses can be found at global.penguinrandomhouse.com.

www.penguin.co.uk
www.puffin.co.uk
www.ladybird.co.uk

First published 2016

001

Set in American Typewriter ITC
Printed and bound in China

A CIP catalogue record for this book is available from the British Library

ISBN: 978-0-857-53514-6

All correspondence to:
Doubleday
Penguin Random House Children's
80 Strand, London WC2R ORL

Penguin Random House is committed to a sustainable future for
our business, our readers and our planet. This book is made from
Forest Stewardship Council® certified paper.